Planning and Scheduling
Made Simple
3rd Edition

By Ricky Smith and Jerry Wilson

Planning and Scheduling Made Simple
3rd Edition

By Ricky Smith and Jerry Wilson

ISBN 978-0-9825163-9-3

Publisher: Terrence O'Hanlon
Cover design: Nicola Behr

For information: Reliabilityweb.com
www.reliabilityweb.com
PO Box 60075 Fort Myers, FL 33906
Toll Free: 888-575-1245 • Office: 239-333-2500
E-mail: customerservice@reliabilityweb.com

10 9 8 7 6 5 4 3 2

*I want to dedicate this book to
my three wonderful grandchildren:
Noah, Abigail, and Caleb Henry.*

– Ricky Smith

*To everyone who has endured the pain
and frustration from working in a reactive
maintenance organization and thought
there had to be a better way.*

– Jerry Wilson

TABLE OF CONTENTS

Those of us who make our living in maintenance and reliability work in a technically oriented field, and the type of people that are drawn to, and excel in, our line of work are typically very detail oriented. Our lot is skilled in analyzing, writing detailed procedures, balancing maintenance budgets, and deciphering reams of data. We dot every "I", and cross every "T". That is our advantage when moving a chaotic manufacturing plant toward an efficient organization with optimum cost and world class reliability. So, why would Ricky and I want to write such a small book, on such an important subject as maintenance planning and scheduling, when it is such a complex subject?

The answer is two-part:

1. We hope to write a second, and perhaps third, small book. In each of these books, we want to cover the key structural elements that must be in place to reap the level of reward that Planning and Scheduling is capable of producing. These books will not be written in an order depicting beginning level efforts in the first book through advanced level efforts in the final. Rather, we will address elements that our experience and research have shown to be the most crucial in improving the effectiveness of not only the Maintenance organization, but also the Operations and Reliability organizations. Whether you believe your organization is world class, failing, in-between, or just starting out in planning and scheduling, we believe this book, as well as future books, will serve as reliable guides in verifying your world class status, helping you get back on track in a failed attempt, or getting started with a solid footing in a new effort.

2. We wanted to create a short series of small books so that organizations wanting to improve their P&S efforts would have a focused, limited number of actions they could easily start on immediately. Sometimes a book presents so many facts and ideas that immediate action gets lost in the myriad of potentials. We plan to present no more than four

or five principles and structural elements of P&S in any of these books.

We believe this approach will help us meet three important goals:

1. The book can be quickly read by people who have demanding schedules and very little discretionary time. Our desire is to present the most important organizational—changing information as concisely as possible.

2. The book will be inexpensive, allowing companies to purchase copies for everyone who has a role in supporting P&S. This advantage should not be overlooked. If every role player in P&S has recently read the same short book, everyone should be much closer to being on the same page, working toward a common goal, knowing what they need to do and what to expect from everyone else. In many organizations, poorly understood roles, initiatives, and goals are a major road block to P&S success.

3. With the concise nature of this book, key concepts and actions will not be lost over the days and weeks that might be required to read a comprehensive book. With a quick read of this book, you will have a few very specific things you can do to expect big gains in effectiveness.

Our title for this series of books reflects our aim, which is to illuminate the simplicity in realizing an effective Planning and Scheduling system. It is our belief that P&S is the single most powerful way in which to improve maintenance effectiveness and that it can be straight-forward and simple to do.

Achieving the ultimate level of improvement from P&S may very well take complex organizations, resulting from months of study, experimentation, process design, and reorganization. However, I believe that there are a few critical aspects to P&S, and until those are working well, nothing else matters that much. When these critical aspects are taken into account and resolved effectively, a simple P&S system can provide exceptional results. I have worked with many organizations across several different industries over the last 15 years and have found that only a minority of those organizations have a P&S system that has made a significant positive impact. In almost every one of these cases, it is due to one or more of these critical aspects. Of the organizations that were achieving significant improvement in their wrench time, many had a very simple approach that focused on eliminating delays.

If you are like most organizations in North America and believe your wrench time is not what it should be, much less what it could be, there is good news. You can achieve significant improvement with a simple and straight-forward approach. This isn't to imply that there is a "one size fits all" answer for P&S. We will point out subtleties to consider for the size of the organization, the crafts involved, the reactiveness of the organization, and over-coming cultural resistance to change. We hope you will find the time you spend reading this book to be enlightening, practical, and beneficial. We look forward to receiving your questions and feedback.

WHAT IS PLANNING AND SCHEDULING

*Key Principle: Have a simple, well-documented, easy to understand process.

As far as P&S is concerned, there are three basic types of work:

1. Emergency Work

2. Routine, Non-Emergency Work

3. Shutdown Work

The key difference is that emergency work must be attended to without delay, whereas the other types of work allow a window of opportunity to plan and schedule the work. Given the time to plan and schedule, a tremendous savings can be created, and that is the ultimate goal of P&S. Emergency work is fraught with delays, misdirection and confusion, but by its very nature we can't take the time to investigate the needs of the job, estimate the resources, develop a plan and obtain the necessary parts that will be needed prior to execution. Instead, we run headlong into the fray, figure out what we need as we go, and sometimes have to back-up and try a different route. This approach adds unnecessary cost to the job, but when Production has been threatened or put on hold, you must demonstrate a bias for action. Putting an end to this type of work is a goal common to Maintenance, Production and Reliability. Therefore, consideration of the objectives of each group is essential. We will review those objectives in chapter 2.

In order for us to get a common view of a simple P&S system, refer to Figure 1. These three types of work must be handled distinctly differently as we will see later.

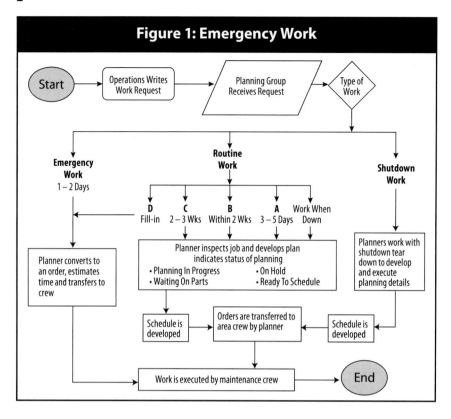

Figure 1: Emergency Work

Emergency Work

Here you can see that for emergency work, the Planner makes a rough labor estimate that includes crafts required, number of individuals needed and total hours per craft. The Planner then sends the work order to the Maintenance crew for execution. For emergency work, this is all that should be done, and it can normally be done without the Planner leaving his office. All that is needed is a labor estimate and to get the job to the shop ASAP.

*Key Principle: Keep the Planner focused on future work only.

Emergency work will be started almost immediately. As a rule of thumb, I include any job that must be started in less than three days as an emergency job. That is a good general practice but it doesn't have to be hard and fast. If a job is easy to plan and parts are readily at hand, or a previously documented job plan is available, it could be fully-planned in time to be placed on the schedule as routine work. The key point is, don't let urgencies cause you to short-cut your P&S process and pollute the system. If you don't have the time necessary to properly plan the job, then it should be handled and counted as an emergency job.

Routine Work

In general, routine work includes all work except for Emergency work and Shutdown work. This is a broad category where P&S normally adds great benefit. Let's look at two particular sub-sets of routine work where there are special considerations that need to be made, "Fill-in" work and "Work When Down".

Fill-In Work

Fill-in work is work that is very simple, can be started, stopped, and re-started with little loss in effectiveness, doesn't involve other crafts and has minimal or no impact to the Production Department. Examples of Fill-in work are:

- Routine inspections that do not require the equipment to be shut down
- Equipment repair/PM that is not Production related
- Repair of spare equipment
- Safety and other types of training
- Etc.

Having a small backlog of Fill-In work is a very valuable tool in managing the overall effectiveness of your employees and your P&S system. Fill-In work is not "busy work"; it should be work that needs to be done and adds value. Fill-In work will serve as a cushion for the remainder of your schedule. If your organization is very reactive, you may find it advantageous to have as much as 20% of your labor scheduled on Fill-In work, in the event that an unknown emergency job comes up.

In a survey we did in conjunction with ReliabilityWeb.com, 29% of respondents reported emergency work to be between 5 and 15%, 24% of respondents reported it to be between 15 and 25%.

The labor scheduled for Fill-In work can stop that work and go to the emergency job. This is much more effective than stopping a fully planned job, where several hours of planning and scheduling have been invested in the work, in addition to the time preparing the equipment, obtaining permits, assembly/disassemble, etc. You also have the cost of rescheduling the job, re-permitting, etc.

Our research has found that interrupting a fully planned and scheduled job typically costs more than 5.0 hours. Of course, this number will vary for craft and organizational differences. I believe this is a conservative number. I have been involved with several organizations where our analysis found that the cost was greater than 10 hours on average for an interrupted P&S job.

Your Maintenance organization can be thrust into a vicious cycle if emergency jobs frequently interrupt P&S jobs. You schedule a job, it is interrupted, and it must be rescheduled, sometimes more than once. Entire schedules get shifted, coordinated efforts are missed, and Production schedules can become impacted. In this situation, all of the value that P&S invested in the job has been lost. It should be your standard practice that a fully planned and scheduled job is the last type of job that will be interrupted to do emergency work.

That is certainly easier said than done in today's environment of tight labor and high demand, but Fill-In work can provide some help. With Fill-In work, a Planner should inspect the job, make a labor estimate, document the necessary parts needed, list any procedures needed, designate the job as "Fill-In", and post it as "Ready to Schedule".

The time required for a Planner to plan a Fill-In job should be much less than the time required for him to plan a normal P&S job. Most Fill-In jobs should be scheduled just like other Routine work. The exception to this is when a fully planned and scheduled job is completed early. In this event, Maintenance personnel should have a list of short Fill-In jobs to choose from to fill the time they have to the end of the shift or until the scheduled time for the next job to start. Managing a schedule without the use of Fill-In work is very difficult. Establishing a clear guideline defining Fill-In work, and using it to fill in the gaps, and cushion your schedule, will make your schedule run much smoother.

Work When Down

You may have noticed in Figure 1, the distinction in Shutdown related work. Many organizations are now doing the same. The work designated as "Shutdown" is the type of work that is done in a planned shutdown or outage event of a designated extended duration. Normally, these events are scheduled weeks, if not months, ahead of time. Whereas the work designated as "Work When Down" is short duration jobs that are planned in advance, with parts kitted, so that when an unexpected shutdown occurs, you have a list of work that needs to be done and is ready for execution. The "Work When Down" backlog should be organized by priority and chronological time to complete (the number of clock hours rather than labor hours). When production goes down for some unplanned reason, with a "Work When Down" list planned and organized in this manner, you can quickly choose work that is most important and fits within the time span provided by the unexpected event.

The handling of Shutdown work will be handled in a later book.

Good backlog management keeps separate backlogs for Shutdowns, Work When Down, and Routine work. Maintenance Managers, Schedulers and Production need quick uncluttered access to these special types of work.

Now that we have considered Emergency work, Fill-in work, Work When Down, and Shutdown work, we can group together any type of work that is left. We could call this regular work or complex work or any number of other names, but unless work in this grouping is specifically designated not to be planned, this work should be planned and scheduled. We will discuss more on Routine work in Chapter 3.

Planning and Scheduling Objectives

What is the Objective of Planning and Scheduling?

That question seems simple enough, however the answer may be one of the fundamental causes for P&S efforts that fail to deliver their potential. Normally, the answer to this question comes from the maintenance perspective and therein lies the problem. P&S is a system more than a process. And because it is a system that extends beyond the maintenance process, the objectives can not merely come from a maintenance perspective. I can assure you that without consideration of Productions needs, in addition to those of Maintenance and Reliability, implementing P&S will resemble pushing a rope, and will likely be an exercise that turns out to be much harder than it should be. Considering and establishing clear objectives for involved organizations is one of the most critical steps in establishing a Planning and Scheduling system that is simple and effective.

From the Maintenance perspective, the objectives are:

1. To leverage your labor resource (get more work accomplished with fewer people).

2. To establish an approach that over the long term will reduce reactive maintenance.

3. To minimize the chaos and efficiency losses resulting from disconnects with the production schedule, priority changes, emergency work, and unanticipated part outages.

The bottom line for Maintenance is that an effective P&S system will enable your maintenance personnel to accomplish more work. This result should be unquestionably obvious in even a moderately successful P&S effort. However, in the recent P&S survey we conducted through Reliabilityweb.com it was revealed that only 10% reported that their P&S was

"Well established and clearly effective". This does not have to be the case. How does P&S enable more effective maintenance? The answer is...by preventing delays during the maintenance process. Preventing delays should be the primary focus of our P&S system. Common examples of delays to be eliminated would be:

- Waiting for the equipment to be cleaned, shutdown, and/or tagged out

- Leaving the job site after the work has started to obtain help, parts, tools, equipment, and/or information

- Interrupting a job in progress to attend to an emergency job, then later resuming the original job (losses would be closing up the original job, terminating the permits, re-obtaining permits, etc.)

- The mismatch of jobs to the length of the work day

- The mismatch between the Maintenance resources, equipment needs, and the production schedule

The first mentioned maintenance objective for P&S is **to leverage your labor resource.** A Planner can inspect several jobs on a single outing, then from his notes and inspection forms, he can order parts for many jobs in only slightly more time than would be required to order parts for a single job. When compared to a Maintenance person looking at the job, returning to the shop to order parts, either going to stores to get the parts or waiting for them to be delivered, a Planner is much more effective. Typically, 45 minutes to 1.5 hours more effective considering time from the moment the Mechanic left the job site until the moment he is back at work on the job site. Similar savings occur from having procedures, specifications, pre-work (insulation removal, electrical disconnect, etc.), and equipment preparation (shutdown, cleaning, tagging, etc.). I have analyzed P&S effectiveness in dozens of Maintenance crews, the savings that P&S yields, as compared to each Mechanic planning and scheduling their own work, typically runs from 3 hours to over 10 hours per average job for Mechanical Maintenance crews.

Each of the common delays bulleted above represent a significant portion of the wrench time losses in your organization. If you have a wrench time of 30%, that means that in an average eight hour day, each mechanic only accomplishes 2.4 hours of productive work. You quickly come to the realization that leaving the job site to get a necessary part is not an effective utilization of a mechanic's time, nor are any of the other above mentioned losses.

If the above mentioned delays represent 30% of your wrench time losses, and through P&S you are able to prevent them, then .3 times the remaining 5.6 hours in the day equals 1.68 hours of additional work that would be accomplished by each maintenance person. In a crew of ten people, this would amount to 16.8 hours each day, and 84 additional hours of work accomplished each week. That is a gain of more than two FTE! While this level of improvement moves this crew to just over the 50% wrench time level (2.4 + 1.68 = 4.08 divided by 8 = 51%), it is not an exemplary level of improvement.

Assuming you had a full time Planner, his time would be leveraged by a factor of two in this example. The 30% losses typically run 40% or more of the total wrench time losses. Also, a full time Planner would typically not be required for a crew of ten. An experienced Planner can typically plan for at least 15, and often-times as many as 25 or more craft persons. In this example, if the Planner was planning for 15 mechanics, then his time would be leveraged 3.15 times and for 20 mechanics, 4.2. You don't get those kinds of returns in the stock market every day! Given this information, why would anyone question assigning someone as a Planner? Perhaps the only good reason for that decision would be that so few organizations are able to attain significant gains via P&S, but that is what we intend to correct. Therefore, given a Planner to Mechanic ratio of 1:15 or greater, and wrench time improvements of 30% or more, you can see how a P&S system can make a maintenance crew significantly more effective. Most organizations would not be able to start out with a Planner to Mechanic ratio of 1:20 but would have to work toward that ratio as the system stabilized and pre-developed job plans were created that could be used again and again, leveraging the Planner's time.

The second mentioned maintenance objective for P&S is **to establish an approach that over the long term will reduce reactive maintenance.** The age old problem in reliability improvement efforts has been to free up the necessary maintenance labor in order to execute the reliability work (proactive work) that will prevent future failures. Without an effective P&S system, it is a constant battle to free up maintenance labor resources from the day to day urgencies in order to execute proactive work. Even with an effective P&S system, it is still sometimes difficult to satisfy both emergency work, and work that is planned and scheduled. But the longer you do it, the easier it will become. How?

Prior to getting effectiveness improvements from P&S, some way or another, you are doing the work that must be done, even if it is mostly reactive emergency work. Some of the work you are doing now could be planned and scheduled. The effectiveness gains that P&S provides will result in those jobs that are planned and scheduled being completed in less time than before. The time saved by P&S creates an opportunity to execute work that will prevent reactive work in the future. Little by little, more proactive work can be scheduled, and as a result, over time, more reactive work, particularly emergency jobs, will be reduced. This will not be an overnight success, but implemented with forethought and perseverance, you will be pleasantly surprised by the results you can achieve in 6 to 8 months.

As an example of how to wedge in a little P&S in a very reactive system to create more time for proactive work in the future, I am reminded of a situation that I was involved in about fifteen years ago. I was a maintenance supervisor over an area that had about 150 centrifugal pumps. When I was first moved to this area, I found that they were extremely reactive. I did a little analysis and found that they were averaging a pump failure every 2.3 days. Making a long story short, we targeted the primary problem that was responsible for our reactiveness and made a commitment to spend any time that we could free up in doing proactive work on those pumps. When we could, we spent our extra time eliminating stilt mounted pumps, standardizing seal types, grouting pump bases, eliminating pipe strain, standardizing on-coupling design, and performing laser alignment using planning and scheduling techniques to cut the time those tasks took. We surveyed these pumps, documented which of these corrective measures needed to be done to each pump and pre-planned these jobs. When a job finished two hours early, or got delayed by a day, we went to the list, grabbed the kitted parts and procedures, and went to work on the corrections. In less than a year, our mean time between failure went from 2.3 days to 53 days. That was a true paradigm change for our crew, and as it progressed, one pump at a time, we had more time to do the things we knew needed to be done. Don't lose sight of the importance of this point; P&S can create significant windows of opportunity. Target how you want to use that opportunity to start steering your organization toward a higher level of proactiveness.

The third mentioned maintenance objective for P&S is **to minimize the chaos and efficiency losses that result from disconnects with the production schedule, priority changes, emergency work, and unanticipated part outages.** This is huge! How often do your maintenance personnel have to regroup because the equipment can't be shut down, operations changes priorities at the last minute, or after the job has been started they realize that the store room does not have a required part? At least 80% of this is avoidable. As we will show, there are techniques and organizational structures that will almost eliminate these losses. The result will be that chaos will be the exception, not the rule, and your maintenance organization will run more often like a well-oiled machine.

Now let's take a look at Production, from their perspective, their objectives relative to P&S are to:

1. Minimize equipment failures that impact the production schedule.

2. Minimize maintenance work that interrupts the production schedule.

3. Maximize the opportunities to perform necessary maintenance congruent with the production schedule.

4. Ensure that maintenance work is attended to that is most important to the Production organization.

As alluded to earlier, implementing P&S without recognizing and capitalizing on the objectives of the Production department, if not totally defeating, will certainly make the effort much more difficult than it has to be. Hopefully at your plant, Production is focused on making product, and if you're lucky, they may also take pride in making simple repairs and inspections on the equipment. Other than that, they pretty much want maintenance to be invisible. They look at maintenance as a necessary evil that intrudes on them far too frequently. Why should they be concerned with P&S? Isn't that something Maintenance should drive?

The first Production objective for P&S that we will look at is **to minimize equipment failures that impact the production schedule.** As I am sure you are well aware, Production hates equipment failures that impact their production schedule. As discussed earlier, P&S is one of the most effective ways to create opportunities to execute proactive work that prevents failures from occurring. It is impractical to think that a start-up P&S effort can immediately start out in this situation. It takes time for the benefits of P&S, coupled with a reliability improvement strategy, to gain sufficient momentum to enable this level of performance in a proactive environment. This subtlety is easily missed. The effectiveness gains from P&S provide the window of opportunity to execute proactive work and the scheduling process actualizes it. The reliability effort provides the activities that should be planned and scheduled. Given consistent effort over time, failures will be reduced, which in turn, will provide time for even more proactive work. Without any of the three (planning, scheduling, and reliability identified proactive work) minimizing failures (reducing the reactive culture) becomes unlikely. Without planning, proactive work is untamable. The duration of the work cannot be accurately estimated since no one has looked at the parts, information needs, additional crafts, and permits required, etc. Without scheduling, the work will likely remain in the backlog, unattended due to the more immediate needs of reactive work, and short term decision making in choosing which jobs to do. Proactive work is not the type of work that demands attention, whereas reactive work is very effective at getting attention. And lastly, without the input from the reliability effort, it will not be readily apparent as to what work will have the desired impact.

The second P&S objective for Production is **to minimize maintenance work that interrupts the production schedule.** Production does not look on maintenance activities that go on longer than expected much more favorably than they do failures that impact the schedule. P&S is the most effective way to minimize maintenance work impacting the production schedule. When jobs are taken through a formal planning process, surprises that will extend the time to complete the job are greatly reduced. Similarly, an effective scheduling process orchestrates the maintenance jobs to the production schedule, minimizing interruptions.

A P&S system where Production is integrally involved provides a communication avenue between Maintenance and Production where both parties are aware of the work that needs to be done, why it needs to be done, how long it will take, what the special precautions or considerations are, and when to best do the work relative to the production schedule. In this situation, maintenance work will be completed in a much shorter time, making it infrequent that maintenance work interrupts the production schedule.

The third Production objective for P&S is **maximizing the opportunities to perform necessary maintenance congruent with the production schedule.** We have already stated the likelihood that Production would like for maintenance to be invisible. However, if you were to go to Production and show that vibration on a critical piece of rotating equipment had increased, that failure was likely within two weeks, and that the job had been thoroughly planned, all parts were on hand, and it would take no longer than eight hours, do you think they would be eager to find a suitable window in the production schedule to perform the maintenance? They most likely would. They would see it as an eminent failure where the impact could be minimized. All P&S work will not be of such importance, or prevent an impending failure, but it should be justifiable and quantifiable. When Production can clearly see what needs to be done, why it needs to be done, what steps Maintenance has taken to prepare for the job and minimize the impact to Production, they will then be more inclined to work with Maintenance to find a window, or in certain cases, create a window in the production schedule so that the work can be executed.

The fourth P&S objective for Production is **to ensure that the maintenance work that is most important to the Production organization is attended to.** Even though Production wants Maintenance to be invisible, there are things they want Maintenance to attend to. And I must admit, sometimes it is a mystery how that work measures up to the other items in the backlog. Nevertheless, I am sure from their vantage point it makes perfect sense. Therefore, Maintenance should do everything they can to attend to Production's needs. In an effective, mature P&S system it really isn't difficult to work things into the schedule. Effective P&S will eventually result in a very proactive maintenance organization where most activities are known and prepared for well in advance and interruptions are the exception.

I remember my first encounter with an organization that had a very good P&S system in the mid '90s. I was at a sister plant site in Longview, Texas for the better part of a week to investigate how they did things. I was amazed. The first thing I noticed was an almost total lack of chaos. The majority of the crew was not being jerked from one job (before finishing it) to another. There wasn't a line of mechanics at the store room counter at 8:30. But the most striking observation I made was that their supervisor, my counterpart, was calm to the point that I could have assumed he was just plain out of touch. His phone wasn't ringing repeatedly to interrupt our discussions, no one came busting into his office to report the most recent failure and the maintenance personnel weren't coming to him to get additional assignments as a result of job completions, or because jobs couldn't be done because Production couldn't, or wouldn't, shut the equipment down. When I met with their Production department, I found that they were very involved in scheduling maintenance activities, at the time that seemed strange to me. Each Production manager I spoke with had copies of the maintenance backlog and the maintenance schedule. Everyone appeared to be committed to the schedule and interruptions to those schedules were infrequent. As the week progressed, I started to realize that maintenance could be something other than reactive, and that P&S had a lot to do with that something. However, I also had a lingering question in my mind, "Could this approach to maintenance work at my plant?" I wasn't sure it could, after all, their production process was completely different from the one at my plant.

Today I know that my suspicion that P&S works well in some manufacturing processes and not in others, was unfounded. When the basic principles are understood, and taken into account, P&S will work anywhere, as you will see as we progress through this book.

Considering the impact to Production that achieving these objectives would have, you can see that when an effective case for change is made with Production in mind, they can be a very strong supporter of your P&S process rather than a disinterested bystander.

From the perspective of the Reliability group, the objectives for P&S are to:

1. Ensure that corrective work, identified by predictive maintenance, is completed within a time frame to preempt Failure.

2. Ensure that Preventive maintenance is completed within identified time frames.

3. Ensure selected maintenance work is completed using Best Practices.

4. Execute maintenance work in a manner that minimizes asset downtime and reduces risk of infant mortality.

The first two objectives for P&S from the Reliability group can be discussed simultaneously. They are **ensuring that PMs and corrective work identified by predictive maintenance is completed within a time frame to preempt Failure.** In many organizations, PMs completed on time runs 50% or less and corrective work, identified via predictive maintenance, is completed on time even less frequently. In lieu of an effective P&S system, this work cannot compete with the day-to-day urgencies of reactive work. An effective P&S system quantifies the job, and its necessities, and then puts it through a scheduling process where the most important work, rather than only the most urgent work, is actively sought out for placement on the schedule. An effective P&S system is the very best way to complete this type of work on-time, on a regular basis.

The third objective for P&S from the Reliability group is **to ensure selected maintenance work is completed using Best Practices.**

As part of the planning process, some jobs will have specific repair/refurbishment procedures to be followed. On equipment types where the Reliability group is trying to improve reliability, they should review the current procedures that the Planner is using, and ensure that those are the preferred methods believed to be most capable of extending mean time between failure. Outside of the P&S process it can be very difficult for the Reliability group to influence repair procedures used by maintenance.

The fourth objective for P&S from the Reliability group is **to execute maintenance work in a manner that minimizes asset downtime and reduces risk of infant mortality.** Executing work that has been through a formal P&S system will take less time than if done without P&S. Also, an effective P&S system will increase the ability to do proactive work that will reduce future failure rates. Thus, asset downtime will be reduced. Additionally, because the planning process improves the ability to use standardized procedures and spare parts for specific maintenance tasks, the Reliability department will be able to provide input to these planned jobs for the equipment they are most interested in, in order for the procedures and parts used to be the most reliable.

The achievement of these objectives from the Reliability group will not only ensure that group's support and participation in the P&S process, but will also ensure the long term success of P&S through reduced emergency and reactive work. If emergency and reactive work are not significantly reduced long term, the success of the P&S system will be in jeopardy due to the resulting inability to successfully schedule the majority of your maintenance labor hours that are available each day (due to urgent reactive work).

*Key Principle: Use these objectives to make P&S a goal common to Maintenance, Production, and Reliability.

How to Plan and Schedule

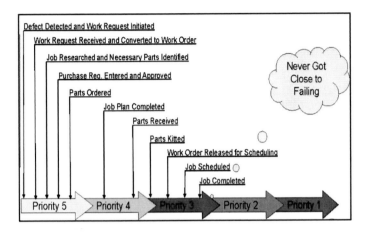

Planning

Simply stated, Planning is the identification of all of the resources required to schedule and execute maintenance work effectively and efficiently. Planning is completed before scheduling.

The start of the Planning process begins when the Planner makes a job site inspection, then starts identifying everything that will be necessary to prevent delays to the job once it is started. The Planner should preferably be a fully skilled craft person who also has the additional skills necessary to execute the responsibilities of Planning. Those skills are:

- Broad technical expertise for the craft
- Detail oriented
- Organized
- Communications skills
- Computer skills

If you think you have to get by with something less than a fully qualified maintenance person then you are selling P&S

short. While all of the skills, in addition to technical expertise, are important, most can be easily learned. Technical expertise will allow a Planner to quickly assess a work request and job site. In short order they will have identified everything that will be needed for an effective job plan. I say effective because I am not one that believes every job plan has to contain a complete list of information, common to all jobs, in order to qualify as fully planned and ready-to-schedule. All of the activities that are completed during Planning and Scheduling are also completed when no Planning and Scheduling takes place. The equipment has to be shut down, parts have to be obtained, etc. A Planner does these activities much more efficiently. Knowing this, why would any organization choose not to use a fully qualified Planner as defined here?

The Job Plan

I believe to be most effective, a job plan should only contain the information that the average Maintenance Technician would need to execute the job at the desired quality level. Any more than that and you start running the risk of the job plan information being ignored. If you want to, you can include reams of data with the job plan, but on the official form, only required information should be present. If your Maintenance personnel are ignoring what is documented in the job plans, it could be a result of too much information that they don't need. If this is happening, they are likely missing key information such as changes that have been made in parts, procedures, specifications, etc. that could be crucial to improving reliability. Therefore, I believe Planners should only include what is absolutely necessary. In our survey, 45% of respondents reported that if they were to place a statement randomly in the job plan, offering $20 to the Mechanic if he would only claim it, the $20 would go unclaimed!

Too many job plans focus on information that the average Maintenance Technician already knows. If we approached job plans a little differently by focusing just on what the Technician needed to know but might not, we may find that the job plans would become more useful. The job summary should use bullets rather than text to list the major steps of the job. Details that a less experienced technician might need can be put in the job package as an attachment and referred to in the bulleted list. When details are put in attachments, it enables most technicians to quickly access the information they need by reducing the amount of information they must go through. Any changes from what the technicians would think of as status quo should be highlighted to draw their attention. With the exception of attachments, you should only use details in a job plan where you are going to require a signature from the technician to show that the work was done exactly as required, and even these details can usually be simplified with bullets. You can make things even easier for your technicians by standardizing on groupings of information and by having no more than seven bullets in each grouping. Additionally, each bullet should have no more than 7 words where possible.

Certainly there are some basics that I would agree must be present for the job to qualify as fully planned, including:

- **Job Scope** – What needs to be accomplished by this job, and what are the basic activities that will need to be executed for completion? If pre-work is needed, like insulation removal, an electrical disconnect, or any other activity that must be completed before the main task can be initiated, the Planner will note that and start making arrangements to have that need resolved before the primary work is scheduled to start. Any follow-up work should be noted, such as jobs to repair equipment that was replaced with spares.

- **Labor Needs** (by craft, skill level, and duration) – The Planner will make estimates for the labor hours, and number of individuals needed, for each craft, as well as an overall estimate for the chronological time to complete the job from start to finish. The minimum skill level required for each craft should also be documented in the job plan. For example, if a second-year apprentice is qualified, that information should be documented in order for the Maintenance Manager to make the most effective labor utilization.

- **Parts** – All of the necessary parts will be identified, and those not stocked in the storeroom, or otherwise unavailable, will be ordered. The job will not be considered as "Ready to Schedule" until all necessary parts are available. Usually, all parts required to do the job will be acquired and assembled in a "kit" a day or two before the job is scheduled to commence.

- **Permits** – Necessary permits will be identified and initiated prior to time to start the job.

- **Procedures** – If a job requires a procedure that is anything other than common practice due to regulatory compliance, reliability, or safe practice rules, it should be included in the job plan package and listed as an attachment on the job plan form. Usually this information will be stored in, or linked to, the Functional Location or Equipment Master in the CMMS, so that the next time the equipment has to be worked on, that information will be immediately available and it will require less time for the Planner to prepare the job.

- **Specifications** – These should be listed when applicable, and in bullet form when possible. For example, if bolts and nuts are stored in bulk in the shop and a particular job requires a bolt of a different grade than normal, that should be listed.

- **Special Tools and Equipment** – These will be noted and assembled for the job.

Some job plans will be created with much more detail because of the complexity of the job. Job plans should be saved by electronically tying them to the functional location for the equipment in the CMMS system (these are known as Pre-Planned Job Packages). In short order, the Planner will have documented plans for the equipment types that fail most often. This will be a big time-saver for the Planner in the future.

The following page is an example of a very simple job site inspection form used by a Planner for a Mechanical Maintenance crew.

JOB SCOPE INSPECTION SHEET

Work Order # _____   Date _____
Equip. # _____   F/L _____
Equipment Type:
Pump____Motor ____Coupling____ Valve____ Tank/Vessel ____Filter ____Dryer____
Piping ____ Other_____
Installation Type: Flanged ___ Welded ____ Screw____ Bolted____Other_____
Fastener Size: Bolt _____ Nut_____Stud _____
Gasket Type: Spiral Wound _____ Gylon _____Teflon _____
Fiber _____ Other _____Size _____
Wrench Sizes: _____
Special Tools: _____
Job Description:_____
_____
_____
Job Scope: _____
_____
_____
Pre-Work Preparation Steps:_____
_____
Safety Hazards: _____
_____
Permits: SW _____OF _____ Entry _____ Electrical Hot Work _____
Excavation _____ Other _____
LO/TO: Yes   No   **Lock Box:** Yes   No   Power Supply _____
Equipment Repair Location Tagged? Yes   No
Digital Pics: Yes   No   **Field Sketch:** Yes   No
Tools, in addition to hand and power tools, include machines and equipment:____
_____
_____
Materials, Description and Quantity: _____
_____
Minimal Skill Requirements: _____
_____
Staffing Requirements: MMs #_____   Hrs _____
                           CSMs # _____   Hrs _____
                           Equip. Oper. # _____   Hrs _____
Follow up Work (Rebuilds, Fabrications, etc.): _____
Post Completion Steps: _____
Name Plate Data:
Manufacturer _____ Type_____
Serial # _____ Size _____ Pressure _____
Model #_____ Figure _____Frame _____
Horse Power _____RPM_____ Amps _____ Volts _____
Temperature_____Drawing # _____ NB _____
Procedures, Specifications, Additional info needed: _____
_____
Prepared by: _____

Here are some key traits of an organization that has an effective Planner:

- Necessary Planner responsibilities do not take a back seat to other needs.
- The majority of a Planner's time is spent working on future work.
- Maintenance personnel seldom have to acquire additional parts on "planned" jobs.
- They have documented the type of jobs that should not be planned in order to increase the effectiveness of their Planner(s). More on this one in a later section.
- They define emergency work and track its level.
- Emergency work is 15% or less of total labor hours.
- Planning documentation is valued and reviewed by the field personnel. Field personnel realize the importance of sticking to the plan for consistency and maintaining the schedule.
- The Planner effectively executes the following responsibilities:
  - ✧ Inspecting the job
  - ✧ Writing a job scope
  - ✧ Identifying parts
  - ✧ Ordering parts
  - ✧ Identifying and assembling necessary procedures
  - ✧ Identifying required permits
  - ✧ Maintaining current status of the work orders and backlogs

Because the Planner is such a skilled and resourceful person, one of those who can always make things happen, it is all too easy for him/her to get saddled with responsibilities that rob time from necessary planning responsibilities. Management must always be wary of this and protect against sacrificing planning quality for convenience. I am not saying that your

Planner cannot have additional responsibilities, rather that Management must ensure that the Planning responsibilities have first priority and that any additional responsibilities do not impinge on them. We discussed earlier how when a Planner's time is leveraged by three or more times, it is unlikely that any other responsibilities assigned to a Planner will have anywhere near that level of value. However, in my experience, it is a common problem that Planners have either been assigned, or they have assumed, other responsibilities that limit the amount of time they have to do their foremost job. Thus Planning quality and/ or quantity suffers. Some common responsibilities that I find Planners fulfilling that do not require a Planner's expertise and could compete with higher value-adding activities necessary for well-planned jobs are:

- Kitting the parts
- Stocking new spare parts
- Maintaining the CMMS information
- Ordering parts for emergency jobs or jobs already in progress. Avoid this one at all costs! It is P&S cancer.
- Restocking shop parts

Scheduling

Maintenance Scheduling is the coordination of the schedule for the maintenance resources (labor, materials, tools, and equipment) and that of the assets (production equipment) in order to:

- Minimize interruptions to the production schedule
- Maximize maintenance work within the opportunities present in the production schedule
- Maximize utilization of the Maintenance labor resources
- Proactively initiate and execute preventive, predictive, and corrective maintenance work
- Maximize wrench time for the Maintenance organization

Each of these bullets has been discussed in detail earlier. So, let's look at how an effective schedule is built. An effective schedule should have an appropriate amount of Fill-in work as discussed earlier. Depending on your organization's level of emergency work, you may need more or less Fill-in work to protect the remaining planned and scheduled work from interruption. The majority of the labor hours available will be scheduled as routine work that has been planned. The remaining minority of the hours will be scheduled as Fill-in work. By design, Fill-in work will be sidelined as emergency work necessitates. 46% of the survey respondents report their P&S jobs are frequently interrupted by emergency jobs. Interrupting Fill-in work does not count as a schedule breaker nor should it require supervision approval. I have seen highly proactive maintenance organizations effectively operate with as little as 5% to 10% Fill-in work, and I have seen those that required 40% to 50%. As a rule of thumb, if your P&S system is properly designed and executed, in 6 to 12 months you should need 20% or less Fill-in work to protect your higher value work from interruption by emergency jobs.

One of the most effective tools in scheduling maintenance work, particularly in a situation where a single maintenance organization serves more than one Production or Manufacturing area, is the use of a Maintenance Coordinator. A Maintenance Coordinator, who reports through the production department, serves as a point of contact for all information and a funnel for setting priorities for Maintenance. I have often seen the case where each shift supervisor, and each production manager, believes his or her maintenance work is top priority. A Maintenance Coordinator can minimize this. A Maintenance Coordinator should attend all production meetings and be thoroughly capable of leveling work order priorities across department lines. The Maintenance Coordinator has knowledge of all production schedule issues such as order ship dates, production start-up and shutdown dates, production delays and product priorities. A representative from the production department, armed with this information, can much more effectively prioritize, help schedule work orders, minimize priority changes, minimize schedule changes, and find opportunities in the production schedule for maintenance work, than all of the Maintenance managers talking with the Production Supervisors in the plant. I strongly believe that the Maintenance Coordinator role is just as critical as a Planner and Scheduler in all but the smallest P&S efforts. In Chapter 4 we will see exactly how a Planner's time is multiplied by a factor of 3 or more and will then calculate a crew's effectiveness gain. In the case of a Maintenance Coordinator, justification for the position should not come from the Maintenance department. A Maintenance Coordinator position should be justified by the Production department. If your P&S system is able to deliver positive gains to your Maintenance Department, a Maintenance Coordinator position will be paid for by the gains delivered to the Production department. The cost associated with an hour for the Production department is much more valuable than an hour of Maintenance department time. Reducing the time required to perform a maintenance job will in turn save the same amount of time for Production. If you have questions about justifying a Maintenance Coordinator, keep this section in mind while reading Chapter 4.

A Maintenance Coordinator working with a Maintenance Scheduler can create a synergy that will cause a paradigm change in the reactiveness of a Maintenance organization. This is the result of the merging of the Production and Maintenance schedules, along with the adjusting of priorities, which will enable more proactive work to be scheduled and completed than without a Maintenance Coordinator.

The last benefit of having a Maintenance Coordinator I will mention, is that of having an advocate in the Production management meetings. The Maintenance Coordinator's allegiance should be to the Operating Department, but his or her participation in the P&S process with Maintenance will instill a high degree of ownership in the Maintenance schedule. Having his or her input in the Production scheduling meetings will be invaluable to the Maintenance organization in getting support for proactive work and for the elimination of delays to Maintenance caused by Production. 47% of our survey respondents reported that Maintenance frequently waits for equipment to be shutdown and/or prepared for work that was scheduled.

*Key Principle: If your Maintenance organization has to struggle with competing priorities from the Production Department and/or a lack of support for the P&S effort, make the case for a Maintenance Coordinator.

Following are some of the key Maintenance Coordinator responsibilities:

- Level work priorities across the department
- Communicate all Production schedules to Maintenance
- Ensure timely equipment preparation for Maintenance
- Delete duplicate and unnecessary work orders
- Help Maintenance find opportunities to complete all proactive work on time

A process that I have seen work very well is for all maintenance work requests from the Operating Department to go through the Maintenance Coordinator before going to the Planner. This gives the Maintenance Coordinator an opportunity to assign a more equitable priority to each work order given his broader perspective across the entire Production department. Going through the Maintenance Coordinator before the Planner also helps the Planner respond to true priorities.

The Scheduling meeting should be attended by the Maintenance Coordinator, the Scheduler(s), the Maintenance Supervisor, and the Planner(s). If the Scheduler has properly communicated with the Maintenance Coordinator and the Maintenance Supervisor prior to the meeting, the weekly scheduling meeting should simply be a final approval of the schedule. I have sat in scheduling meetings for a large maintenance organization that were very well prepared for and took only 15 minutes. It was very impressive. The people in those meetings were very good at what they did and they came to the meeting prepared. They had a well-defined process and everyone followed it. I have also sat in scheduling meetings that were either unorganized, ill-prepared for, involved turf wars between Maintenance and Production, or were simply games being played out because management required the meeting. I have seen these meetings take from one to four hours.

Daily versus weekly scheduling, which is better? I believe that for the most effective scheduling, both should be used. That doesn't mean that you have daily scheduling meetings. I think you can do both with only a single weekly scheduling meeting.

This allows a weekly schedule, agreed upon in advance that provides the overall target for the following week; then daily updates as needed. Daily changes, if any, are usually small. What this will do for your organization is provide increased flexibility to meet needs unforeseen when the weekly schedule was built. Inflexibility is one of the key downfalls of a rigid scheduling process. Keep in mind, the scheduling process should be very rigidly adhered to; however, that process can have some degree of flexibility designed in. For example, let's assume it is Tuesday morning and an Operator just reported a blower making an odd noise. A work order is written and the Planner inspects the job. The Planner determines that a bearing needs to be replaced. Also, since there are several of these blowers in the plant, there is a documented job plan that was previously created. For this job to be fully planned, all the Planner has to do is order the bearings and set the status to "Ready to Schedule." All of the remaining information will already exist in the pre-planned documentation. Using the process described in Figure 2, the job can be placed on Wednesday's schedule as long as everything is ready by 1:30 pm. This is making the scheduling process work for you rather than punishing the organization that doesn't have the flexibility to count this as a planned and scheduled job. The Planner wasn't rushed abnormally, and the job plan has the necessary elements of a fully planned and scheduled job.

Figure 2 is an actual scheduling process from a plant that has a mechanical maintenance crew and a control system/ electrical crew, each with their own Maintenance Team Manager. These two crews maintain three separate production areas that operate around the clock seven days per week. Each production area has its own Maintenance Coordinator. There is

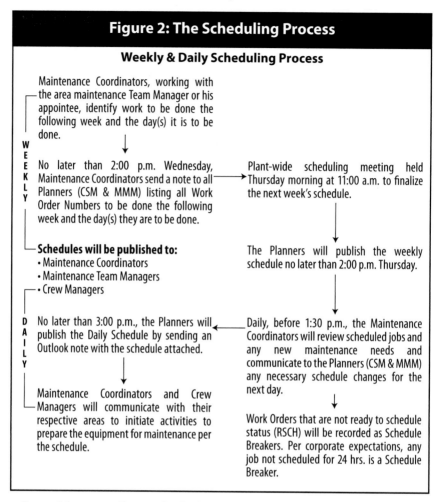

Figure 2: The Scheduling Process

Weekly & Daily Scheduling Process

WEEKLY

Maintenance Coordinators, working with the area maintenance Team Manager or his appointee, identify work to be done the following week and the day(s) it is to be done.

No later than 2:00 p.m. Wednesday, Maintenance Coordinators send a note to all Planners (CSM & MMM) listing all Work Order Numbers to be done the following week and the day(s) they are to be done.

Schedules will be published to:
• Maintenance Coordinators
• Maintenance Team Managers
• Crew Managers

Plant-wide scheduling meeting held Thursday morning at 11:00 a.m. to finalize the next week's schedule.

The Planners will publish the weekly schedule no later than 2:00 p.m. Thursday.

DAILY

No later than 3:00 p.m., the Planners will publish the Daily Schedule by sending an Outlook note with the schedule attached.

Maintenance Coordinators and Crew Managers will communicate with their respective areas to initiate activities to prepare the equipment for maintenance per the schedule.

Daily, before 1:30 p.m., the Maintenance Coordinators will review scheduled jobs and any new maintenance needs and communicate to the Planners (CSM & MMM) any necessary schedule changes for the next day.

Work Orders that are not ready to schedule status (RSCH) will be recorded as Schedule Breakers. Per corporate expectations, any job not scheduled for 24 hrs. is a Schedule Breaker.

a Crew Manager for each shift to manage production issues. The entire group (about 8 people) gets together for their weekly scheduling meeting. With these clarifications, the process is fairly self-explanatory. In this particular organization, the two Planners also served as the Schedulers.

Some situations you want to prevent from being counted as scheduled include: when a rush to meet a deadline results in a poor quality job plan; or when your Planner is still creating or amending the job plan while work on the job is underway. In my opinion this is a cardinal sin. When your Planner is Planning the job while work is in progress on the job, that isn't future work. His time is not being leveraged. You should only use the Planner's time where it will be leveraged (more about this in the next chapter). If work is in progress, a regular maintenance person should be executing all necessary activities from turning wrenches, ordering parts, and finding procedures. Once work starts, you have missed the opportunity to leverage a Planner's time. This is an essential principle that must be understood and practiced.

Scheduling cutoff times is a critical piece of an effective scheduling process. In Figure 2, you will notice there are two separate cutoff times. The first is the cutoff to get work on the next week's schedule which is 2:00 pm Wednesday. The second cutoff time is 1:30 pm daily for updates to the next day's schedule. Cutoff times are necessary in order to "Publish" a schedule. With a firm day and time, the Scheduler can electronically issue an official schedule for either the next week or the next day, whichever the case may be. There aren't separate schedules; the weekly schedule is updated daily. Once published, the Production Department can start planning to make the necessary preparations to the equipment before Maintenance arrives at the job site. Depending on your type of industry these activities may include:

- Shutting the equipment down

- Cleaning/decontaminating the equipment

- Preparing permits to work on the equipment (lockout/tag out), etc.

Maintenance can also begin a myriad of activities. For example:

- The parts clerk can start kitting the parts for jobs a day or two before execution time.

- Maintenance can look at the schedule and start planning their personal activities.

- The Planner can change the status of the work to "Scheduled" and discontinue tracking those jobs; they will now effectively be in progress.

Without a cutoff time, it would be impossible to publish a schedule, causing an almost endless amount of back and forth communication between all involved in the process to execute a job. 48% of survey respondents report using a formal cutoff time for creating a schedule. Only 41% of respondents report publishing a schedule electronically, available to all. Notice in Figure 2 that this organization had a firm rule that in order for work to be counted as scheduled, it had to be on the schedule for at least 24 hours. This particular organization had historically "punched the card" by regularly listing work as planned and scheduled when it clearly had not been, thus management created the 24-hour requirement in an attempt to improve the quality of Planning and Scheduling. Normally, I would not suggest a 24-hour requirement such as this.

*Key Principle: Publish a weekly schedule electronically that is available to any who may need the information; then, update it daily as results and demands change.

Can Planning and Scheduling be treated separately, or must they be implemented together? Yes to both questions!

- Planning prevents delays by identifying the needs of the job.
- Planning enables Scheduling, by quantifying the resource needs in order for a block of time to be set aside to do the job.
- Scheduling enables effectiveness by maximizing resource utilization in both Maintenance and Production.
- Scheduling alone can improve effectiveness with only an estimate of labor needs by reducing the down time between maintenance jobs, eliminating false starts when Production can't free up the equipment, and by reducing the downtime when Maintenance has to wait while Production shuts down and prepares equipment.
- Together, P&S are much more effective on certain jobs.
- Not all jobs are candidates for Planning or Scheduling (this will be detailed in the next section).

Ultimately, you will want the majority of your work to be both planned and scheduled because this is how you will get the most effective increase.

Some work, however, is not well suited for Planning and thus will only be scheduled. One example is Fill-in work and Inspections. Planning would not be done beyond a basic labor estimate, which should always be documented to enable effective scheduling and backlog management. The major consideration would be if the work was very straightforward and only required "free issue" parts (parts stocked in the shop) or no parts at all. Then the job would only need to be scheduled. Running jobs such as this through the planning process would not add value. In this case, more time would be required to plan than would be saved by delays.

The characteristics of a job that present the opportunity for savings are complexity and predictability. Complexity can come in the form of technical difficulties, multiple crew involvement, special permits, special equipment or tools, special procedures and multiple part/material needs. It is complexity that creates the opportunity, if not the likelihood of delays. And, it is on the prevention of delays that we want our Planner focused. The more labor that is required by a particular job, the more value a half hour of savings can be worth. If you save one person a half hour by having a part ready before the job is started, versus saving 10 people a half hour, it can make the difference in whether a job should be planned or not. If the Planner would spend more than 30 minutes inspecting the job, updating status, ordering parts, etc. then he has used more than the 30 minutes saved, in the example of a one-person job. You must protect your Planner from these types of errors. Very simple and/or short jobs do not have much value that can be added via planning, so they would normally not go through the planning process. This practice frees the Planner to focus on jobs where planning can leverage his time by three or more times.

Predictability is a term I use to describe when the parts, man-hours, technical skills, and other resources the job will need can be accurately identified. Jobs that have low predictability are not good candidates since a Planner would not be able to accurately predict the resource and part needs for the job or may not be able to estimate the amount of time a given job would require to be completed. A good example of this sort is some jobs for an instrumentation crew. Take for instance, a level transmitter work order. In inspecting the job, a Planner will not be able to determine if the fuse is blown, the probe is bad, or if an amplifier or communication card needs to be replaced. In this case, the Planner would not be able to specify the parts for the job or how long the repair might take. The best that can be done is to make an "average" time required estimate and stop the planning there. There will be more on how to handle these sorts of jobs later in this chapter.

When to Plan, When to Schedule

A tool I have found useful in helping to build the mind-set to effectively determine which jobs should be planned and/or scheduled is the Complexity/Predictability Matrix shown below. Shown on the y-axis is Complexity. As the Complexity of a job increases, the opportunity and likelihood for delays increase. The other aspect that helps determine if a job should be Planned and/or Scheduled is whether or not those complexities are Predictable. Predictability is represented on the x-axis.

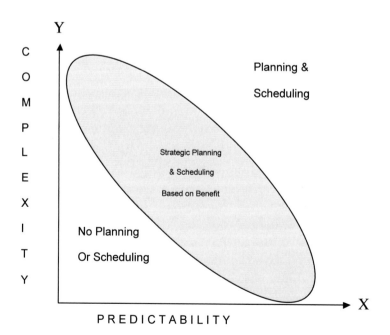

When a job is both complex and predictable P&S can provide tremendous leverage. These jobs, due to the complexity, have many potential delays and because those delays can be accurately assessed, they are highly predictable. Therefore, the delays can be effectively prevented yielding significant savings. A savings of 3 to 5 times or more as compared to the time the Planner will spend on the job are easily obtainable.

As Complexity and/or Predictability decrease on a given job it becomes more and more important to be strategic on the planning and scheduling effort in order to maintain a positive benefit from P&S. Even though there may be potential delays with a job, only the predictable delays can be handled by standard P&S actions. The Planner who is cognizant of this can utilize his time much more effectively. When a job is not complex and not predictable there are essentially no savings that a Planner can add to the job, so there should be no planning or scheduling at all. Usually jobs of this type are of short duration and may use free issue parts and do not require permits.

We want our Planner focusing on as many complex and predictable jobs as possible because that is where the Planner's time is leveraged the most. Unfortunately, not all of the work that comes into the backlog will be of this type. Therefore, we need to provide some guidance to our Planner so he or she can quickly determine which jobs should be planned and scheduled, which jobs should be planned only, which should be scheduled only, and which jobs should not be planned or scheduled.

Refer to the matrix as a guide to help identify the appropriate P&S strategy. When a job is neither complex nor predictable, you should not plan or schedule the work. This work can be handled as Fill-in work usually. As in this case, when the work is not predictable, it is not appropriate to schedule because you won't know if it is a 2-hour job or an 8-hour job but, you can assign several of these types of jobs (blocking) that will be at least one day's worth of work and show the 8 hours of labor on the schedule. Because this category of jobs on the matrix is very simple, it is not worth a Planner's time to inspect and plan it. Therefore, the Planner should identify the work as the type that will not be planned (Fill-in work) and move it out of the Planning backlog.

P&S for Jobs That Are Somewhat Complex and/or Predictable

Now that we have covered why jobs that are both complex and predictable should be planned and scheduled and why those that are not complex or predictable should not be, let's consider how best to handle jobs with a mixture of complexity and predictability.

When a job is somewhere other than the lower left or the upper right of the matrix, your Planner needs to recognize that to be effective, he will need to be strategic when planning any given job. If, on these type jobs, the Planner follows the standard planning routine, trying to complete all of the required items for a planned job by listing the parts he believes will be needed, the number and craft type etc., the results when the job is executed will likely be less than satisfactory. Attributes that are not predictable will either have the wrong item or wrong information provided. Delays will still occur. This is the downfall of requiring a particular set of information for a job to be considered "Planned." The Planner needs to recognize that on the attributes of the job that are predictable he can apply standard planning techniques. However, on attributes that are not predictable, the Planner may need to take compromising actions or elect to only plan or only schedule a job.

Compromising actions are a trade-off where actions are taken that would normally not be most effective but in special situations are more effective than taking no Planning actions. Examples would be on work where it is not possible to accurately identify man-hours, or when scheduling blocks of work can be more effective than scheduling individual jobs. For example, if you had a job that will require any where from four to twelve man-hours for two technicians, rather than scheduling an average number of man-hours for the individual job, a Planner could schedule four of these jobs. This way, even if all four jobs only took four man-hours each, or two clock hours, the two technicians would have a full day of work. Depending on the job specifics, it may be appropriate to let the technicians work on the jobs right up until the end of the shift or, it may be more appropriate to have them start on a fill-in job when they complete a job after 1:00 pm or some appropriate time within a few hours of the end of the shift. This would be assuming the impact of potentially starting a subsequent job and not being able to finish it, particularly if Production was impacted, may be undesirable. It may be much more important to finish a job once it is started and if so, use a strategy like this on jobs where the man-hours are not predictable.

Scheduling Based on Man-Hours Alone

Many organizations use a rule of thumb to determine whether or not a job is a candidate for P&S based at least in part on total man-hours. Regardless of the level of Complexity of a given job, if the estimated number of man-hours meets the minimum criteria for a planned and scheduled job and those hours are deemed predictable, then the job should be Scheduled regardless of any other attributes of the job. As we will show in the next chapter, it is imperative to be aware of the man-hour losses associated with all of the other attributes of a job. However, as we have covered previously, an accurate schedule for a given maintenance crew has additional benefits beyond the face value of scheduling a particular job. Excluding man-hours, all other aspects of planning a job should be justifiable at face value, that is, the prevented or reduced delay is greater than the time required by the Planner.

Matrix Area – Low Complexity, Medium-to-High Predictability

Some jobs may not require enough hours to warrant Scheduling, but they could have one or more other losses that are predictable. In this event, if the losses would cost more time than would be required for the Planner to plan the job, the Planner should plan it. If the job will not require an interruption to Production, once planned, the work can be treated like Fill-in work. If a Production interruption will be required then, the job should be Scheduled, even though the man-hours fall below the minimum.

Matrix Area – Medium-to-High Complexity, Low Predictability

Let's now consider a job that is medium complexity and low predictability. An example of such a job could be repairing an automatic valve. In this case, the time to repair could be anything from 1 hour to 8 hours depending on the failed component. The parts required could be a pilot valve or an actuator, or a solenoid valve or the valve itself. If the valve has to be replaced, that would require a line break which would require additional activities by Production to flush the line and tag that section of line out. This last scenario would also require additional PPE and additional Permitting. There are many jobs that fit this category. If you utilize a standard P&S approach many delays will still occur. There are several ways that these types of jobs can be approached to ensure that delays are reduced or prevented. If the automatic valve is a very common type, a standard parts kit can be created that would include any of the parts that logically fit the problem description. An exception might be to leave the actual valve out of the parts kit because of the significant expansion of scope a valve replacement would entail. Valves typically would be of various sizes and material of construction and therefore may not be suitable to provide in a standard kit. If this is the case, once it is determined that the valve is the problem rather than some component, a new job could be initiated. Otherwise, the parts kit can be an effective way to prevent parts delays. On the job summary, a section should be included that lists each part included in the kit with a check box to show which parts were used so the kit can be restocked for the next job. The next consideration for this job is if you have decided to treat the valve replacement as a new and separate job, then how does that impact the man-hours that may be required for the possible job scenarios, excluding the valve replacement? If it greatly narrows the range of time the job could require, it may now be within the allowable tolerance (Predictability is much higher) to be considered for scheduling an individual job. If not, it should be scheduled in blocks if sufficient numbers of like jobs exist. This could necessitate a Technician to work outside his normal work area in order to have enough jobs to schedule him for a given time period, usually one-half of a shift or a full shift. This brings up an important point. Organizations that have successfully reaped the benefits of P&S usually have not allowed themselves to be limited by existing paradigms. For example, shop A takes care of this area, and shop B takes care of a separate area. Where jobs such as this are not compatible with the standard thinking toward P&S, they recognize that to leverage their maintenance technician's time they may need to say that jobs of a certain type will be executed outside the limitations of the standard shop responsibilities by packaging several jobs of the same type across shop boundaries.

This level of commitment to improving an organization's level of effectiveness will result in astounding changes in performance. In summary, your P&S staff should:

- Consider the Complexity and Predictability of the jobs they consider for P&S

- Schedule jobs greater than the minimum man-hour cutoff when the hours are predictable

- Plan those activities that are predictable and will prevent more loss than planning time required. Don't worry about supposed requirements for a job to be considered "Planned." If you have identified the losses that can be prevented and have taken the necessary planning steps to prevent them, then the job is "Planned."

- Consider compromise actions that will still save time on identified losses that can't be accurately predicted. These may be parts kits that include all parts that could cause the symptom, blocking assignments, recognizing when jobs may need to be divided into separate jobs in order to prevent delays in most situations, and thinking outside the normal boundaries of shop assignments. This is not an all inclusive list and as you work through a wrench time study, more situations and the ways to overcome them will come to light.

Some rules of thumb to use in determining jobs not suitable for Planning:

- Labor hours of job – usually 4 to 8 hours are needed before payback for a Planner's time is possible
- The job needs to be complex and predictable, both in diagnosing the problem/parts and the labor

Criteria to use in determining jobs that may not be suitable for Scheduling:

- Jobs that are of short duration
- Jobs that do not require production equipment to be shut down
- Jobs that do not require any preparation before work can commence
- Jobs meeting these criteria are often Fill-in work

As a general rule, we want to consider planning any job that is not an emergency where any of the following apply:

- More than one craft is involved in the job.
- Storeroom or outside purchase materials are needed.
- Multiple permits are required.
- A special maintenance skill is required.
- Production will have to be interrupted.
- Boom truck, crane, or other special equipment will be needed.
- There are special tool needs (example - welder, alignment equipment, etc.).

Each maintenance group should review their types of work and define the work that should not be planned, and the work that should not be scheduled. All other work should have some form of planning and/or scheduling. This is a very important step that will leverage both the Planner and Scheduler's time by preventing them from spending time on low-value-adding activities.

To see a graphical representation of how Planning and Scheduling work together, see Figure 3. On the left, you will see the various pieces of information the Planner collects for the job scope. Also note that a side benefit from the Planning process is CMMS corrections and updates. In a good P&S system, the Planner will be a key provider of information for CMMS equipment file updates. On the right, you will see all of the information the Scheduler draws on to create an effective schedule.

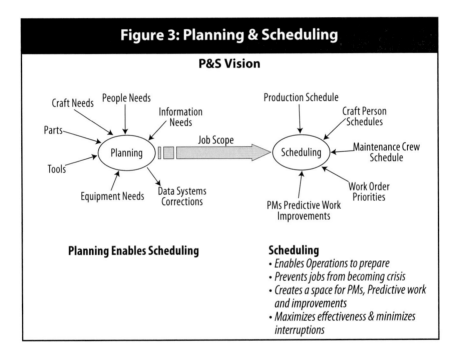

For Planning and Scheduling to work efficiently and effectively, everyone from the planner/scheduler to production management must understand what a well-defined maintenance process looks like, and how Planning and Scheduling impacts this process. In traditional maintenance, we find a very reactive environment in which a planner/scheduler has no place.

The planner/scheduler role in this environment is mainly used to expedite parts for emergencies. See Figure 4 for a

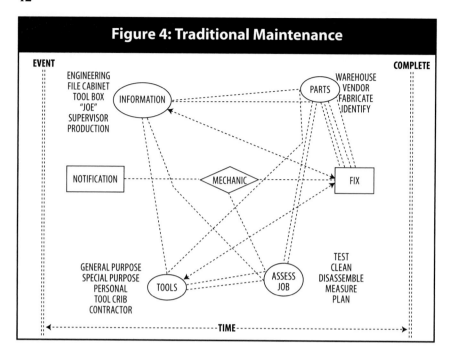

Figure 4: Traditional Maintenance

picture of traditional maintenance. The Planner is seldom working on future work. In this figure you can see the loss created by multiple trips for information gathering, to the shop for tools, and to the storeroom for parts. Contrast this with Figure 5 where an orderly system is created by P&S.

In a proactive environment, the planners/schedulers are focused on future work and are not involved in reactive issues in maintenance. Most of their work comes from the visual inspections, predictive maintenance data, and other proactive tools which we will call "Preventive Maintenance." In the gray box in Figure 5, you can see where most work should be coming from. It should not be coming from work requests on failed equipment, or worse yet, emergencies. In a proactive environment, we do not want to see failures unless we have determined failures are acceptable on that specific equipment.

In proactive maintenance, Planning and Scheduling provides the greatest benefit to workforce efficiency and effectiveness, and thus higher asset reliability.

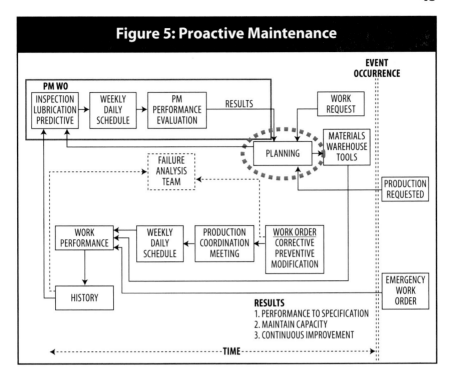

Figure 5: Proactive Maintenance

Here is a brief review of the benefits you can expect from P&S:

- A minimum gain of 3 maintenance FTE per Planner for a Planner to Crafts person ratio of 1:15 or greater

- Reduced reactive maintenance

- Improved reliability resulting from consistent maintenance methods

- Reduced production schedule interruptions

- Improved completion of Proactive work

- Reduced "Emergency" jobs

- Reduced inventory cost for maintenance spare parts. As maintenance becomes more proactive, failures will be reduced, thereby reducing the need for multiple spares

- Reduced cost for "overnight" shipping costs and expediting fees

Obstacles to effective P&S you should anticipate:

- Operations will view P&S as being of secondary importance, and they should. Their concerns should primarily be on production, but armed with the information covered in the section on their objectives for P&S, and gaining full involvement in the process via the Maintenance Coordinator, they will find sound reason to support and participate in Maintenance Planning and Scheduling.

- It will be easy to focus on superficial (activity) measures in monitoring P&S and lose sight of the structural necessities (leverage of a Planner & Scheduler) that actually make it work. We plan to elaborate more on P&S measures in a later book, but for now I will say that most P&S measures are centered around % labor hours or jobs planned, % of jobs or labor hours scheduled, and then % of jobs or labor hours completed as scheduled. There isn't anything inherently wrong with these measures except that they only give a superficial picture of how things are going. They really don't say anything about whether or not the anticipated delays were actually prevented. The planning measure assumes that if the job was planned, all of the delays were prevented. Nothing could be further from the truth. In my experience over the past several years assessing the P&S systems of many maintenance organizations, I have found that this situation is so typical it is almost predictable. And when that is the case, the P&S system often is not delivering significant effectiveness, if at all. The same is largely true of the Scheduling measure. The number reported is also assumed to indicate that effectiveness was improved simply because it was reported to have been scheduled. Again, even though the job was scheduled, did the time estimate match the actual time the job took within reason? Did Production have the job prepared prior to the arrival of Maintenance personnel, or did Maintenance personnel have to wait? Were the permits initiated prior to their arrival? Are the jobs scheduled in time for the necessary preparatory activities to be accomplished? I have seen organizations that showed any scheduled job completed anytime during the week, as being completed as scheduled. In that case, how does Production know when to be ready, or another craft know when their interface will be ready or needed? I would be willing to bet the farm that someone is waiting, and if that is the case, the P&S system is not doing what it should. I hope I have made my point. I refer to these measures as "activity" measures. Something is going on, but you can't really say if the activity is good or bad without additional information. You must find a way to at least occasionally audit your system to see if delays are being sufficiently prevented. Otherwise, you can expect to be one of the 90% in our survey of roughly 100 companies that reported they were uncertain if their P&S system was making a difference or not. Much more will be discussed on this topic in the next chapter.

- Reactive work – already sufficiently discussed.

- Plans are not being followed by the craft persons. In the event that plans are not being followed by your craft persons, then you can accurately assume that the hour estimates your Planners are making are not matching the actual hours spent on the job. After all, different methods would take longer or shorter, wouldn't they? Also, different methods may require different parts. In this event, you can be confident that delays are being introduced. Schedules are built to harness the highest percentage of the craft person time available. If different methods take longer, the succeeding job is not started on time and a cascading effect is started that can easily impact the rest of the week. If the different method takes less time, at first glance you might think that this would be a good thing, but odds are that saved time is not realized, but lost. If an interface with a different crew or a helper situation in a successive job is scheduled, what does the person do with the saved time? They wait. Ideally, if they indeed have a better method, they should get the Planner to shorten the time estimate for the job, but often the savings is simply a shortcut because they didn't think a certain step was necessary. As you learn more about P&S, you will appreciate more and more the analogy of an orchestra and the need for everyone to be playing from the same music (the job plan) while following the lead of the conductor (Scheduler).

- Identifying the jobs where Planning, in particular, is not beneficial. There are some jobs that are not worth a Planner's time, and then other jobs that just can't be accurately planned. These types of jobs need to be identified in order for your Planner to not waste his time. His time can't be leveraged if he is spending time on these types of work.

If implementing P&S is so simple, why do so many organizations struggle with it? Because little or no appreciation for, or understanding of, the systemic structure that results in their current level of effectiveness is present. What I mean by this statement is that too often P&S is started with little or no understanding of the types of delays that should be eliminated, and how much of your organization's time is lost in those delays. Without this information how can you know where to focus your efforts? How can you know if you really are getting better or not? You can't. Additionally, in many organizations P&S is Maintenance driven, conducted, and measured. Production has little concern or involvement in the P&S efforts. In short, beware of the following three big mistakes:

1. Focusing only on "activity" measures

2. Not understanding wrench time and its causes

3. Production not playing an integral role in the P&S process

Here is a quick look at the traits of the organizations who responded to our survey who appear to have successful P&S programs:

- Critical roles assignments:

  ◇ Planner – 92% of respondents have designated Planners

  ◇ Scheduler – 92% of respondents have designated Schedulers

  ◇ Maintenance Coordinator – 55% have designated Maintenance Coordinators

- Their craft person to Planner ratio is 20:1 or more.

- Planners are protected from the urgencies of day-to-day maintenance

- Planners and schedulers are centralized.
- Their Maintenance Coordinator report through the Production chain of command in order to effectively prioritize and provide the time to plan and schedule work.

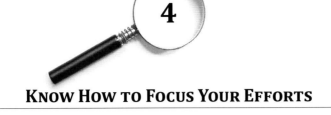

KNOW HOW TO FOCUS YOUR EFFORTS

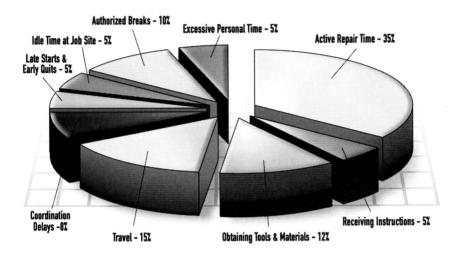

Just because you create high-quality job plans and maintenance schedules, you can't assume you are creating value. The effectiveness of Planning and Scheduling can only be understood with the knowledge of delays that are actually prevented.

In our 2007 survey through Reliabilityweb.com, 68% of respondents reported that in their opinion their P&S effort was successful. When asked how they knew it was successful, 25% reported an improvement in wrench time, 16% reported an improvement in Maintenance cost as a percent of plant replacement value, and 51% reported a reduction in backlog. Each of these are reasonable indicators of an improvement in performance, however, only wrench time can provide you with the knowledge of exactly what improved, why it improved, and by how much.

What is wrench time? Wrench time is the actual time, usually expressed as a percent of an 8-hour day, that Maintenance personnel are actually doing work. Not just any work, but the specific work defined by their primary role. For example, a Mechanic's time would be counted as wrench time if he were repairing a pump. However, if he was looking up a part number for a seal he needed to replace, or going to the store room to get the seal, or gathering some necessary information, that would not be counted as wrench time. Meetings, training, travel, clerical duties, communication, all would be classified as non-wrench time. As you can see, it is not practical to think that 100% wrench time is possible. However, that isn't a problem, studies show that the wrench time of North American industries is between 25% and 35% on average. Any improvement in wrench time is an improvement in Maintenance effectiveness; you are getting more work done with the same labor force. Planning and Scheduling are the very best tools to improve wrench time.

Why Do a Wrench Time Study?

Before diving headfirst into the details of a wrench time study, let's look at why we need to go to the trouble of doing one. Many experts put forth the idea that P&S can double your maintenance effectiveness, and I believe that is true. But, it is also true that a significant percentage of the organizations that implement Planning and Scheduling never achieve significant benefits. Some even lose effectiveness by implementing it. How can that be? Isn't P&S bullet proof, in that it is guaranteed to create paradigm changing results? Unfortunately, if you only focus on increasing the percent of planned work and the percent of labor that is scheduled, and you create staff positions to facilitate P&S then it is very possible to lose effectiveness, and without a wrench time study it may not be readily apparent. Situations such as this are often the result of focusing on P&S as a solution rather than as a tool. The solution is preventing the occurrence of delays.

Being able to make P&S simple begins with understanding that P&S is only a tool, not the solution or goal. Planning and Scheduling is simply one of the tools that can help us be more effective at maintaining the physical assets of the plant in which we work. As is the case with all tools, P&S has a specific purpose and application. If used at the right time, in the right way, P&S can lead to a paradigm shift in maintenance effectiveness. If used as a generic program to "do maintenance right" it will be no different than blindly using Preventive Maintenance to solve all of your reliability problems. The results will not be as desired unless the tool is used correctly.

This may be a point that gets lost by many people who focus on P&S as if it had the intrinsic ability to guarantee significant results. Rather than setting your primary goals around specific P&S activities such as % man hours scheduled, I think goals that would provide a better indication of real progress would by things like:

Improved maintenance effectiveness as measured by

• Wrench time

• Overtime

• Backlog weeks

• Equipment reliability (Mean Time Between Failure)

• Fewer production interruptions due to equipment failures

• Reduced maintenance cost as a percent of equipment replacement value

• Other goals that indicate more productive results are occurring

Goals like these can keep us from being deceived by basic P&S measures that only indicate a given activity is occurring at a given rate, but gives no indication if delays are actually being eliminated. You should never lose sight of the fact that the elimination of delays is the primary benefit you can achieve from P&S. At face value, standard P&S measures like "% completed as scheduled" do not give you any assurance that maintenance personnel did not have to wait for permits to be completed or wait for another craft to complete an activity before they could start, or any other number of potential delays that could have occurred yet not derailed the job completely. I have worked with more than a few organizations which had very good numbers on their P&S measures but their true effectiveness had not improved significantly. I think if we clearly understand why this can be true, then we can understand how we can get the full benefit of P&S.

If we have an understanding of the specific types of delays that are causing the majority of our effectiveness losses, then we can have a better perspective of what our measures may not be telling us. Knowing this would also show us where we can get leverage from P&S in order to be more effective.

In Chapter 2, we reviewed the basic mathematics of how P&S can increase your wrench time. In the example used, the crew went from 30% to 51% by increasing their wrench time by 1.68 hours (from 2.4 hrs to 4.08 hrs) for each Maintenance Technician. An analysis of this type gives no indication of what was done to yield the improvement. After analyzing many Maintenance organizations I now have the firm belief that if you don't know the specific type of losses that you need to eliminate, you are much less likely to get positive results via P&S. Simply Planning and Scheduling as much work as possible may or may not necessarily yield this level of improvement. If not, then how?

Improvements in wrench time come from identifying specific types of delays and then taking action to prevent those delays. Let's look at an example:

Reviewing the example from Chapter 2:
If initial wrench time is 30% then,

.3 X 8 hours per day = 2.4 hours of actual mechanic work daily.

8 – 2.4 = 5.6 hours of loss each day for each mechanic.

A 30% reduction in the loss via P&S = 5.6 X .3 = 1.68

1.68 times 15 technicians = 25.2 extra hours of work accomplished per day!

2.4 + 1.68 = 4.08/8 = 51% new wrench time

In order to actually get this much gain, rather than simply implement P&S and then hope for the best, we must learn what the specific losses are that once prevented, would make up the 1.68 hours of gain. A wrench time study will reveal where your losses are.

As an example, let's assume the following losses were identified in a wrench time study. Times are an average per occurrence:

45 minutes due to waiting on Permits

60 minutes on obtaining parts

45 minutes while transitioning from one job to the next

60 minutes due to special needs (specifications, drawings, procedures, etc.)

60 minutes due to interfacing with other crafts

These were actual losses observed in a Mechanical Maintenance crew in a chemical plant. In other industries, observed losses could be significantly different. Permitting in any process industry can be a complex activity and it may not always be possible to have the permits completed prior to the arrival of Maintenance personnel to the job site. Even so, the aim should be to minimize the amount of time Maintenance has to spend waiting for and completing permits, all the while ensuring adequate safety precautions have been taken. Obtaining parts and transitioning from one job to the next are probably applicable without regard to industry, although the amount of loss can still vary. "Special needs" are losses that may not apply to a wide variety of jobs, thus the "special" designation. These losses occur when special situations arise like needing a bolt torque spec for an unusual size bolt, or needing a drawing, procedure, or piece of equipment. Losses due to waiting on other crews, as an example could be waiting until paint containing lead is abated, insulation removal takes place, or a motor is unwired, etc. Conducting a wrench time study enables managers to see the exact causes of delays, their frequency, and why the delays are as long as they are. With this information, the managers will be able to make much more accurate estimates of the extent to which these delays can be reduced.

Here are the results of the manager's estimates on how much the delays can be reduced, based on the wrench time study:

Permits 45 min. 80% reduction = 36 min. saved or 0.6 hrs

Parts 60 min. 75% elimination = 45 min. saved or 0.75 hrs

Job transition 45 min. 75% reduction = 34 min. saved or 0.57 hrs

Spec needs 60 min. 25% elimination = 15 min. saved or 0.25 hrs

Craft Interface 60 min. 20% reduction = 12 min. saved or 0.2 hrs

In the example on **Permits**, the 45 minutes will be reduced on average by 36 minutes, or stated another way, we will go from an average of a 45 minute delay to that of only 9 minutes. I haven't chosen this amount of reduction arbitrarily. After conducting a wrench time study and careful consideration with field personnel, it was decided by the managers that this was a reasonable amount of time, on average, for the Mechanic to review the tag-out process and sign the permit.

It was decided that **Parts** delays could be eliminated on 75% of the jobs that are Planned and Scheduled. On those jobs there shouldn't be any delays due to obtaining the parts for the jobs. This would save 45 minutes averaged out over all of the jobs that were Planned and Scheduled. You will notice that in this example, an estimate has been made that all parts can not be anticipated on as much as 25% of the jobs that are Planned and Scheduled. Actual conditions at your plant may be different.

Losses encountered during **Job Transitions** will be reduced by 80%, so instead of it taking an average of 45 minutes between jobs it will only take 11 minutes.

Special Needs for jobs, which are specifications, drawings, special tools, or equipment like a man lift or a boom truck don't apply to every job that is Planned and Scheduled, but when they do, the losses can be significant. In this example from a Mechanical Maintenance crew in the chemical industry, when this category applies, the average loss is 60 minutes. Also, as shown by our wrench time study these needs only apply to 25% of the jobs that are Planned and Scheduled. Therefore, if these losses are prevented, we would save an average of 15 minutes per P&S job. 60 X 0.25 = 15 minutes for the average job.

Interfaces with Other Crafts can also be a significant loss. And, like Special Needs, it will not apply to every job that is Planned and Scheduled. In this crew we found that when there are craft interfaces, the average loss is 60 minutes. We also found that 20% of the jobs that are Planned and Scheduled have these losses. Therefore, we could save 12 minutes on average by preventing these delays. 60 X 0.20 = 12 minutes.

In aggregate, we find that these specific delays account for an average of 142 minutes or 2.37 hours per job that can be saved by targeting our P&S efforts toward prevention of these specific delays. In reality, you might not be able to achieve all of these savings. However, I believe that you should identify a challenging yet realistic amount of losses that can be prevented. As you implement your improvement strategies, you can track your progress with targeted performance audits of your wrench time. In the end, you may or may not achieve all of the identified savings but, you will be obtaining the rewards of the new performance level resulting from any savings that you are able to obtain, and it will have a significant impact on your effectiveness. Even small gains in wrench time yield large benefits when multiplied by the number of Maintenance personnel working in the improved system as we will see next.

Now, let's take a look at the overall impact to this crew as a result of improved effectiveness. The crew from the example in Chapter 2 had 15 Mechanics, but in order to do P&S we took one of the Mechanics and made him a Planner/Scheduler. That leaves 14 Mechanics to do the work, let's assume that the Planner/Scheduler is full-time. This crew averaged 13 hours per work order. If the delays can be prevented as estimated, then 13 hours average per job – 2.37 savings = 10.63 hours, the new average per P&S job. If you only averaged working 7 of the 14 Mechanics on P&S work, which would be a very small amount then, 7 X 40 hrs = 280 man-hours. They will average completing 26.34 jobs each week, 280/10.63 = 26.34. Whereas, without P&S the same 7 crew members would only have completed 21.5 jobs per week on average. That means 4.8 more jobs are going to be completed each week on average. If this happens, one of the primary benefits assigned to P&S implementation is that you will see your backlog go down significantly over time.

Originally, this crew's wrench time was 30%. Let's look at what the wrench time is now and what it could be in the future if more personnel could be assigned to P&S work.

Earlier we saw the crew in the example originally had the following effectiveness:

.3 (30% wrench time) X 8 (hours per day) = 2.4 hours of actual mechanic work daily. The loss per day per Mechanic would be 8 – 2.4 = 5.6 hrs.

If we have averaged an additional 2.37 hours of wrench time for each person that is assigned to P&S work, then their wrench time is now 2.4 + 2.37 = 4.77 hours per day for a new wrench time of 59.6%. The 7 mechanics in aggregate have a gain of 16.59 hours per day, 7 X 2.37 = 16.59. If we subtract 8 hours for the one Mechanic that we made a Planner/Scheduler then we have 8.59 hours left of total gain, or an improvement of just over one full person, 8.59 divided by 8 = 1.07 FTE (full time equivalent) of gain. In this case, the Planner has effectively doubled his value. If we were to assign 11 of the 14 Mechanics to P&S work our gain would be, 11 X 2.37 = 26.07 hours each day or 18.07 hours after accounting for the Planner/Scheduler. That is a gain of just over 2 FTE Mechanics. You would be adding 2.26 Mechanics (18.07 divided by 8 = 2.26) to the crew for no additional cost of labor. In this situation the Planner/Scheduler will have tripled the impact of his efforts! In this case, with 11 Mechanics on P&S, 11 multiplied by 40 hours per week = 440 man-hours, divided by the new average per

P&S work order of 10.63 = 41.4 jobs completed per week as compared to 33.8 jobs completed with no P&S (440 divided by 13).

Estimated wrench time for the two scenarios above would be:

30% for the 7 Mechanics of the crew not on P&S, and 59.6% for the other 7 would result in 0.3 + 0.596 = 0.896/2 = 0.448 x 100 = 44.8%

For the scenario with 3 on unplanned/unscheduled work and 11 on Planned and Scheduled work:

3/14 = 0.214 X 100 = 21.4%

11/14 = 0.786 X 100 = 78.6%

(0.3 X 0.214) + (0.596 X 0.786) = 0.0642 + 0.468 = 0.533 X 100 = 53.3% wrench time for the crew as a whole. Here, the crew's effectiveness was almost doubled, from 30% to 53.3%!

This shows how a Planner's time can be tripled with Planning and Scheduling. With 11 Mechanics on P&S, the Planner pays for his own time plus 2¼ more Mechanics. An average savings of 142 minutes may seem overly optimistic; however, in light of the 13 hour average per job, this is only an improvement of 18.2%. For mechanical maintenance, coming from a state of no Planning and Scheduling, this is not an uncommon level of improvement. Depending on the craft and complexity of the work in a given crew, improvements of 25% and more are not uncommon. Only with the information and understanding that a wrench time study can give you is this level of insight and targeted improvement efforts possible. As this demonstrates, P&S has a huge multiplier effect when it is used to target specific delays. I can't overstate the importance of performing a wrench time study. It will take considerable planning, time, and effort to do, but afterwards, you will know exactly where your problems are, what they are costing you, and you will have a very good idea of how to prevent the losses going forward. Without a wrench time study you are shooting in the dark and guessing at your progress. Additionally, with the type of information a wrench time study provides to an organization, it should be easier to gain the support of all parties involved in order to achieve significant results via P&S.

Now, the question is, how do we get this type of information that will show us exactly where our problems are and what they are costing us?

General Considerations for a Wrench Time Study

Actual wrench time can be a very difficult measure to gather, requiring many hours of observation and study. A much simpler, but still useful measure is First Wrench Time (FWT). FWT is a measure of the maintenance delays at the first of the shift and gives a very good indication of the overall wrench time. Best of all, FWT is relatively easy to acquire. The downside is that you must assume that the effectiveness measured first thing in the morning is representative of the delays that might occur throughout the day, or you can strategically identify the delays that may be occurring later in the day and find a way to assess those without going to the pains and expense of a full wrench time study.

First, let's look at a First Wrench Time study and then we will look into ways of identifying the effectiveness losses that may be happening later in the day. Figure 6 shows the FWT audit form used to collect the data mentioned in the following paragraphs.

Figure 6: FWT Audit Form

First Wrench Time Observation Data Sheet

Observer: _____

	Date	Day	WO #	Crew	Desired Start	1st Wrench	Time Lost	Code*	Reason
1									
	Job Scheduled		Yes	No					
	Job Planned		Yes	No					
2									
	Job Scheduled		Yes	No					
	Job Planned		Yes	No					
3									
	Job Scheduled		Yes	No					
	Job Planned		Yes	No					
4									
	Job Scheduled		Yes	No					
	Job Planned		Yes	No					

Codes		Codes	
10	Equipment not prepared	40	Permits not prepared
15	Tools not staged	45	Waiting on other crafts
20	Parts not staged	50	Operations contact not available
25	Equipment not staged	60	Attended meeting
30	Needed info not staged	100	Other (please add description in comment field)
35	Process not down		

A FWT assessment would indicate the average time it took Maintenance personnel to actually get started on a job in the morning as observed via random audits conducted weekly. The assessment will show you how much time is lost in travel to the job, waiting for the equipment to be shut down or prepared for Maintenance, waiting for permits, gathering information, etc.

For example, in a FWT assessment I helped do that was conducted on a Mechanical Maintenance crew in a chemical plant, we found that the most frequent delay was waiting for the permits to be completed. The average delay was just over 40 minutes. To make matters worse, this delay was present in 35% of the Planned and Scheduled jobs that were observed. This was clearly a significant problem. Now armed with this information, it was relatively easy to garner support, develop an action plan, and gain improvement, which should then have been verified by a follow up FWT assessment.

After conducting an FWT, as you analyze the data, it will be clear which data is likely comparable throughout the day, which pieces of data will likely be worse, and which will likely not be as significant. One piece of information that is a little harder to get accurately first thing in the morning is the amount of delay due to obtaining parts. If you only observe the job until First Wrench Time, you can't really know if all of the parts that ended up being needed were identified by the Planner and kitted.

I have found that many CMMS systems can provide a report that will show all part purchases throughout the day and whether they were delivered or picked up at the stores counter. A little analysis of this data—comparing work order numbers to the daily schedule—should reveal to what extent parts are needed on jobs that were in progress. Considering the logistics of the job relative to the job site, the parts information, and the storeroom, the parts ordering process that the Mechanics have used, and whether the parts were delivered or picked up at the store room, you can get a good indication of the amount of delay and frequency of the delay to assess the impact to wrench time. There will likely be additional types of delays that will occur throughout the day that you will have to consider and then find a way to quantify them. Surveying the maintenance personnel may provide key insight into the other delay types that you will need to assess.

As your management team works on this process, I believe it will become evident that a well-planned FWT assessment with targeted assessment for losses later in the day can give a clear indication of a particular crew's actual wrench time. Knowledge of an overall wrench time, as determined by a FWT study and targeted assessments, can add valuable perspective into the crew's effectiveness. But the most powerful information is the specific data on individual delay types. This is where you can focus action plans and gain valuable performance improvement. This information will also be invaluable to your Planner and Scheduler, enabling them to make their efforts more effective.

*Key Principle: Know the types and extent of the delays in your Maintenance process before starting a P&S effort or implementing improvements to an existing process. Measure and maintain your success with follow up FWT studies.

How to Conduct a FWT Study

I am sure there are many good ways to conduct a FWT study, here is one. I participated in a FWT study a few years ago in a Maintenance Department that had four separate crews, a Department Head, and one Reliability Manager. The six of us committed to making two random audits each week for five weeks. The four crew supervisors conducted their audits in their respective areas. The Department Head and the Reliability Manager conducted their audits across all crews. This plan gave us 12 data points per week and a total of 60 audits at the end of the fifth week.

Depending on the level of delays, an audit could take 45 minutes or longer. As an auditor, you must be prepared to stay at the job site until you can observe that the desired work has started (normally, wrenches turning).

The afternoon before, or the morning of your audit, select a job to audit from the list of planned jobs scheduled for that day. Or if your organization hasn't started P&S yet, find a job to observe that will start first thing in the morning. Be at the job site first and wait for the Maintenance worker(s) to arrive. Upon their arrival, record that time, then patiently wait and observe for the start of actual work. After work has clearly started, question the workers on reasons for any delay and complete the data sheet appropriately.

Two weeks into the study, the 6 managers who used the audit form above found that they needed additional categories and also needed to break down existing categories to specifically identify losses. Plan to amend your audit form and recalibrate managers one to two weeks into the audit process. It may be helpful to do a few audits as a group of managers rather than individually.

Sometimes a job will involve troubleshooting as an initial activity rather than turning wrenches. In these cases, once an auditor has determined that the mechanic is on the actual task of the work order (troubleshooting to identify the problem) and that the avoidable delays are no longer in play, the start time should be recorded. The managers involved will need to discuss the various situations and agree prior to the observations on how they will consistently count first wrench time as being started.

Communication to the Field Personnel

Without effective communication to the field maintenance personnel, these audits can result in a negative impact to morale; however, this type of audit is not much different than safety audits and observations you may already be doing. These audits are to determine any avoidable causes of delay in the progress of the job, and therefore, the mechanic should not perceive this as a reflection on his or her individual performance. Most of the delays are "system" caused rather than by an individual. System theory says that at least 80% of what people do is because of the system they work in. Therefore, we should be very careful to not punish individuals during a wrench time audit for personal work habits. Any personnel problems we might run across will be small in comparison to the delays we will find that are system caused. If the maintenance personnel are comfortable with the audit process, you will get good data. If not, their reaction to your presence will inadvertently mask some losses.

Before implementing this process, Maintenance management should go to each maintenance shop and discuss what they plan to do using this section as a guide of things to cover. Explain what wrench time is and why it is so important. Point out that management is not trying to get people to work harder in order to accomplish more work, but wanting to prevent delays so that Maintenance personnel are interrupted less and the work goes much smoother. Success will mean that Maintenance personnel will be spending time on much higher value activities. Review the process with them, the data you are after, the audit form, and most importantly, solicit their ideas. Be sure to answer all of their questions.

Using this chapter as a general guide, you will be richly rewarded for your efforts in identifying wrench time losses.

GUIDING PRINCIPLES FOR PLANNING AND SCHEDULING "KEEPING AN ORGANIZATION FOCUSED"

"Focusing an organization's efforts is the only way to achieve and maintain success"

Guiding Principles are principles an organization must follow in order to be successful in any area where there may not be proper alignment. Planning and scheduling will never be effective without the alignment of Production, Maintenance, and Engineering.

Guiding Principles keeps an organization focused and the success of planning and scheduling hinges on these principles. Planning and Scheduling Guiding Principles are developed together with leadership in Production, Maintenance, Maintenance Planning, Maintenance Scheduling, Reliability Engineering, Maintenance Engineering, and Project Engineering. Developing these principles together as a team allows an organization to be aligned in their efforts and ensure success of Maintenance Planning and Scheduling.

Planning Guiding Principles

- All "critical" work will have effective work procedures developed.
- All PMs/PdMs (not regulatory) must address specific failure modes.
- Planners focus only on future work.
- Bill of Materials must be developed for all Critical Equipment.
- Production and Maintenance must be aligned in the planning process:

◇ Roles and Responsibilities

◇ Expectations

◇ Metrics

Scheduling Guiding Principles

• Planned Jobs must have all parts on site and kitted before being scheduled.

• Production notifies Maintenance immediately of equipment availability changes in order to provide the maximum time possible to plan, prepare and schedule maintenance activities.

• We shall perform an after action review on any unanticipated shutdown that exceeds the threshold for downtime significance.

• We must manage the backlog:

◇ Total

◇ On Hold

◇ Work When Done

◇ Ready to Schedule

◇ Planning

◇ Waiting Parts

◇ Shutdown

We hope this book has been helpful, simple, and to the point. Please send us your comments, questions, and suggestions for topics to cover in the future. You can contact us at: Jerry Wilson, jerrywilson@ffcmail.com and Ricky Smith, CMRP, ricky-smith@comcast.net.

GLOSSARY

Emergency Job – A job that, if not attended to immediately, would result in missed customer orders, excessive product losses and/or serious safety risk. Emergency jobs automatically warrant overtime to complete as soon as possible, including calling in extra maintenance personnel if needed. Emergency jobs can interrupt the daily schedule with the appropriate level of approval.

Fill-in-Job – A simple job that requires little or no preparation by the Production Department or Maintenance. These jobs can normally be started and stopped with little loss in effectiveness. Time will be estimated on these jobs by the Planners as a minimum planning activity. Parts will normally not be kitted.

First Wrench Time (FWT) – A measure that represents the amount of time lost between when a maintenance person theoretically could begin work and when he actually did. The losses represented can occur from poor preparation, inadequate scheduling and insufficient planning. Examples are: "had to wait on permit", "had to go up to see what I would need", "had to wait for equipment to be shut down".

Full Time Equivalent (FTE) – This represents one worker for one year's worth of work. Forty hours per week times 52 weeks equals 2080 hours. This is a theoretical constant used to calculate maintenance effectiveness.

Maintenance Coordinator – The representative to the Maintenance Department from the Production Department. Their responsibility is to serve as a single point contact for prioritizing and coordinating all maintenance issues with the Production Department. The Maintenance Coordinator should report through the Production Department and be knowledgeable of all production priorities, schedules and needs.

Planned Job – A job that has been inspected prior to execution to determine and document the job scope, crafts, man hours, permits, parts, tools, procedures and technical information required to complete as effectively and safely as possible.

Planning – The act of assessing a job, prior to execution, for the purpose of identifying and eliminating delays, both common and unique.

Routine Job – A non-emergency job that has some degree of complexity in the preparation, coordination and/or execution of the job. These jobs are normally good candidates for planning and scheduling.

Schedule – A document that defines the chronological sequence of work assignments and completions for a particular Maintenance and/or Production area. Example, a schedule published at 3:00 pm Thursday afternoon for the following Monday through Friday time period that identifies the jobs and job start/completion times for a particular maintenance crew.

Schedule Breaker – An emergency job that interrupts a routine job that was planned and scheduled. A measure should be kept on Schedule Breakers documenting the number, the area, and the reason for the emergency job. Interrupting fill-in jobs is not a schedule breaker. Any job that interrupts a scheduled routine job should be designated as an emergency job.

Scheduled Job – A job where all activities, parties, and departments involved have been coordinated at a specific time and day for maximum convenience and effectiveness. Interruption of the schedule should be the very last option taken to meet the needs of Production. The majority of the savings that can be gained from scheduling will be lost if the job is not done at the specific time it was scheduled to be done.

Wrench Time – An industry standard effectiveness measure that indicates the ratio of time that a maintenance person is actually performing the desired task versus time viewed as a loss, (waiting on permits, obtaining parts, soliciting help, rounding up necessary tools, giving advice on another job, etc.) This measure can be difficult to obtain accurately.